S0-BVN-685

TO GEOFFREY REES SUGARMAN

PICTURE BOOK OF ELECTRICITY

BY JEROME · S · MEYER
ILLUSTRATED BY RICHARD FLOETHE

LOTHROP, LEE AND SHEPARD · NEW YORK

Library of Congress Catalog Card Number: 53-6738

✦

THE WORLD WITHOUT ELECTRICITY

IMAGINE FOR THE MOMENT that you are living on the tenth floor of an apartment house in New York or some other large city. You settle down in a comfortable chair in the early evening and start to read. All of a sudden the lights go out. You strike a match to find your way to the door and go out into the hall to ring the elevator bell because you want to go down to see the superintendent. But the bell doesn't ring. After waiting a while for the elevator, you decide to walk down ten flights of stairs (in the dark with nothing better to light your way than matches). You arrive at the superintendent's apartment on the ground floor and find him in a terrible mood. You ask him to phone the light company to send a repair man but he tells you that the phone is dead and the lights are out and the bells won't ring and the elevator won't run and his flashlight won't light and

he can't find out what is the matter with everything because he can't get any news on the radio. That, too, is dead.

You decide to leave this gentleman to his fate and go down town to the emergency division of the Light Company yourself. As you walk into the street the silence and the darkness startle you. There is not a light anywhere but with the aid of the full moon, you are able to see automobiles and street cars and buses. They are as still and as dead as everything else. No cars or buses can move, so you jump on your bicycle and pedal through the dark streets to the Light Company's office. When you finally arrive, the man in charge breaks the sad news to you:

"We have just learned from a secret messenger that there is no electricity anywhere in the world! All radio and TV broadcasting is dead, and all the newspaper presses are shut down because they are run by electricity. From now on, everyone will have to get used to walking, or riding on bicycles or in horse-drawn vehicles because automobiles and airplanes cannot run without electric sparks from spark plugs. Business houses will have to close for they can't go on without trucks and buses and telephones. And even if they could go on, what kind of business could they do when all mills and factories everywhere are shut down for lack of electric power? Every electrical instrument, all over the world is dead and won't come to life until electricity returns to run our world once more."

From this imaginary condition which, of course is impossible, you can get some idea of the importance of electricity in the every-day life of everyone in the civilized world. Without it we should all be living back in the days of our great-great-great-grandfathers, without any of the modern luxuries and conveniences we all take for granted. Of course there could be no movies or radio or television. All modern methods of communication would stop. All letters would have to be carried by men on horseback, or taken over long distances by steam locomotives. It would take a week or more to get news from Europe or even from coast to coast in our own country. Since all manufacturing would be crippled without electricity, the many wonderful and attractive toys and gifts you can buy now would gradually disappear or sell for prices so high few people could afford them. Tall buildings would become useless without elevators, so our great cities might become ghost towns. We could go on and on picturing how strange and inconvenient a world without electricity would seem to us today, and proving how

CROCKERY
CITY POWER

much our civilization depends on electric power but it is not necessary, since you very likely know how much it means to us all.

Since this is true, it is a good thing to learn why electricity is so powerful and important to us and to become better acquainted with its "younger brother" MAGNETISM. Magnetism is tied up and bound up with electricity—wherever one is, the other is sure to be. For example:

THE HORSESHOE MAGNET

Everyone knows what a horseshoe magnet is. You have undoubtedly played with one many times and had lots of fun watching needles, small nails, tacks and other little bits of steel or iron jump right up and cling to it. You probably know that the ends of two arms are called "poles" and that one pole is entirely different from the other. One of the poles contains positive magnetism which we indicate by the plus sign (+) and the other contains negative magnetism which we indicate by the minus sign (—). These two poles are always attracting each other.

If you had two magnets just exactly the same size and you brought the two together so that the — pole of the first magnet touched the + pole of the other as shown in the picture, you would feel a great pull and would find it difficult to separate the two magnets because there would be such attraction between them. If now, you turned one of the magnets around so that the two + poles came together all the attraction would vanish and it would be just like touching a nail to another nail. There would be no attraction at all. You can easily prove this to yourself if you buy two horseshoe magnets at any hardware store and try this simple experiment.

So we see that opposite poles always ATTRACT each other while similar poles never do. In fact, similar poles actually push each other away or REPEL one another. This is so important that it would be well to memorize it so you'll never forget it. Just say this over to yourself several times:

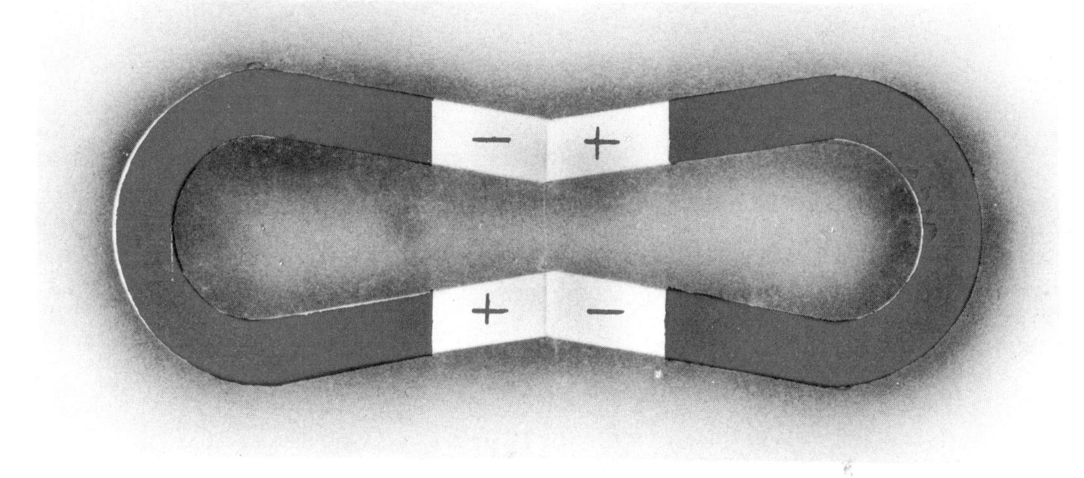

"Opposite poles always attract each other
Similar poles always repel one another"

WHY DOES A MAGNET ATTRACT IRON?

But why does a magnet attract a nail or a needle or any other piece of iron or steel? They are NOT magnets. They have no + pole or − pole. They are just neutral pieces of iron or steel and nothing more. So why are they attracted to the magnet? The answer is that the magnet sets up a kind of invisible magnetic field in the space immediately surrounding it, and any steel or iron that comes within

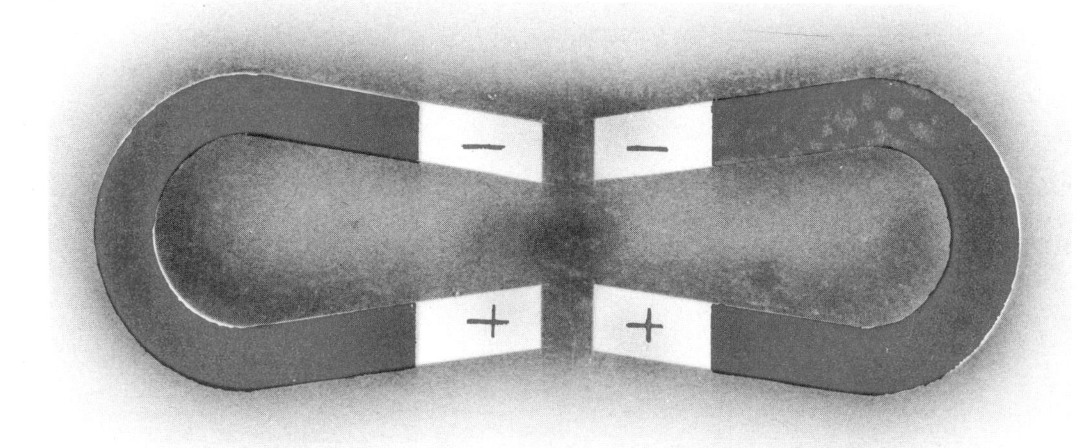

that invisible field is instantly transformed into a tiny magnet in its own right. Each tiny invisible speck which we call a molecule of iron or steel is actually a magnet, but the billions of magnetic molecules are packed helter-skelter so that they neutralize one another. When a large magnet comes near them, all the + poles of these molecules point one way and the − poles the opposite way, and the piece of iron or steel instantly becomes an independent and tiny magnet with a + and a − pole all its own. The molecules in that section that come close to the + pole of the big magnet, small as they may be, immediately turn their negative poles toward the big magnet. And the molecules in the part that comes close to the − pole of the big magnet immediately turn their positive poles toward the big magnet. Since these opposite poles attract each other the small pieces of iron or steel jump up and cling to the magnet. That is why a magnet attracts nails or needles or any other little piece of steel or iron. As soon as a nail or a needle is removed from the magnet it loses practically all of its magnetism and becomes just a little piece of iron or steel once more.

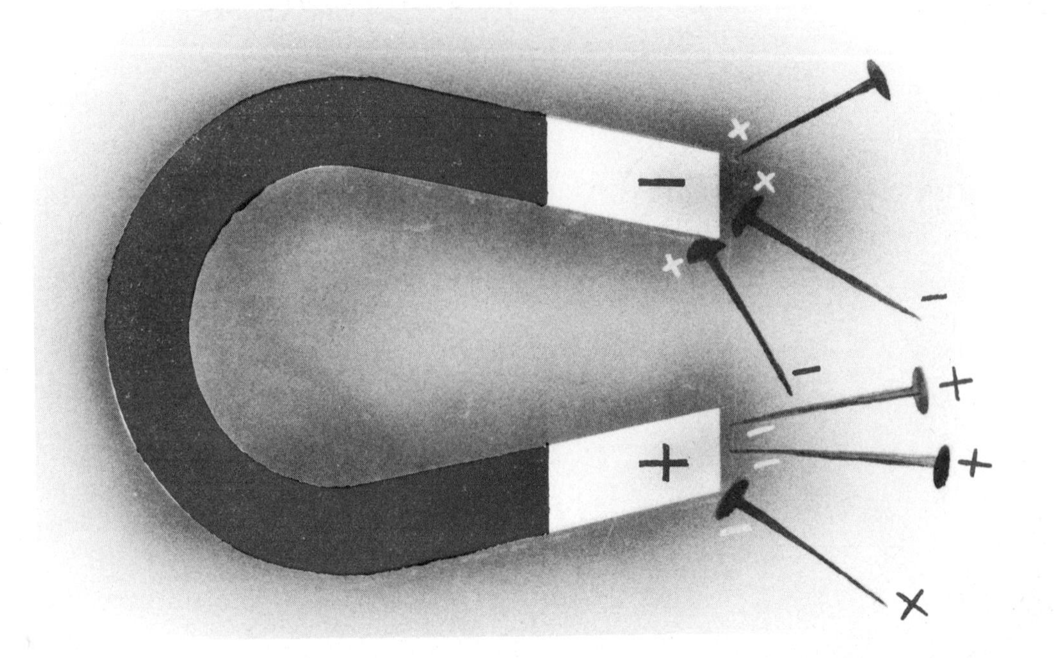

TRY THESE TRICKS AND AMAZE YOUR FRIENDS

Before we begin to discover the many fascinating things about electricity, here are a few tricks which you can do without any preparation at all. And you can entertain your friends by doing them.

The first trick is extremely simple but be sure to try it on a cool or cold day: Ask a friend to spill a tiny bit of salt from a salt shaker onto a smooth wooden table. Just turn the salt shaker upside down once so that very little salt spills out. Now challenge your friend to pick up all that salt without touching either it or the table with anything. He must pick it right off the table yet he can't touch either it or the table. He will say this is impossible, and indeed it would be if it were not for the magic of static electricity. When he gives up, just take a hard rubber comb and run it through your hair five or six times very quickly; then bring the comb near, but not touching, the salt. Instantly all the salt grains will jump up and cling to the comb the way a needle or nail does to a magnet. You will then have picked up all the salt without touching either it or the table.

The second trick is even more mysterious. You can stick an ordinary playing card to the wall without using any glue or paste or any other kind of

"stickum." And you won't use any nails or tacks or pins either. You'll just place the card against the wall and it will stay there *all by itself!* All you need do is hold the card in your hand and scrape your feet along the carpet as you move to the far corner of the room. As you draw close to the wall, at that end of the room, slap the card quickly right up against the wall and it will stay there, apparently held up by nothing at all. It's just like magic and it will always work provided you don't try it on a damp or hot, or even warm day. You can do this over and over again, "sticking" cards all over the wall without hurting the wall in the least and, at the same time, astonishing your friends.

A DIFFERENT KIND OF MAGNETISM

Now let us consider just what actually *did* happen in these two tricks and, later on, we shall find out just *why* it happened. In the first trick, you transformed an ordinary hair comb into a "magnet." As a matter of fact, it was much better than a magnet because it wasn't nearly as "choosey." A magnet will attract only iron and steel, while this "comb-magnet" will attract almost any thing that is very light, like a ping-pong ball, salt grains, hairs, threads, tissue paper and lots of other light objects. And there is another very important difference between this "comb-magnet" and a real magnet. The comb is not a magnet and never was a magnet until you rubbed it on something. If you hadn't run it through your hair rapidly five or six times it would never attract anything. You made it "magnetic" by rubbing it on something. As soon as you did this it was able to attract light objects and hold its power of attraction for a short time. In order to make the comb attract light objects ALL the time you would have to keep rubbing it on something. As soon as you stop, all the "magnetism" in it will start to die out. A magnet, on the other hand, never needs to be rubbed to make it magnetic. It is, and always will be, a permanent magnet.

It is important to notice that the comb, when rubbed, not only acted as a magnet, but it created a *magnetic field* in the space immediately surrounding it and any light object that came within that field was attracted to the comb just as any light bits of steel or iron that came within a magnet's field became attracted to the magnet. There will be more about this magnetic field later on but it is most important right here to remember that it actually exists.

In the second trick you transformed an ordinary playing card into a sort of "magnet" which was attracted to, and stuck to, the wall. You know very well that the card would not stay on the wall by itself without having anything done to it. So you *did* something to that card even though you may not realize you did. By scraping your feet along the carpet you produced this mysterious "magnetism" in your body and transferred it to the card because you were holding it. The card, then, became "magnetic" by being in contact with you and you became "magnetic" by scraping your feet on the carpet. If you hadn't done this nothing would have happened and the card would never have stuck to the wall.

So you actually produced a different kind of magnetism in a few ordinary objects like combs and cards. You could do it with other objects as well but we will use these two to illustrate what we want to say. How did you produce this kind of magnetism? You did it by *rubbing* something on something else. You simply have to rub the objects quickly and briskly on the carpet or on hair or cloth or cat's fur to make them magnetic. Now this rubbing and scraping does require a certain amount of energy on your part and this energy, which we call *mechanical energy,* was transformed mysteriously and almost magically into a different form of energy called *electrical energy* so important in electricity.

Like magnetism, electricity occurs in two forms: positive(+) and negative(—), but instead of calling them poles we call them CHARGES. We say an object is charged with positive electricity or it is charged with negative electricity. We speak continually of *positive charges* and *negative charges* instead of positive poles and negative poles as in the case of a magnet. So the comb and the card were charged with negative or positive electricity. This created an electric field all around them and gave the same general attractive powers that a magnet has for steel.

It is impossible to produce electricity without some kind of movement. Something must move against something else, or must overcome some sort of resistance in order to furnish energy which in turn, will be transformed into electrical energy. In the cases we just discussed you had to rub the comb or scrape your feet on the carpet to produce static electricity in these objects. In the case of the electric current that comes into your home, huge generators or dynamos are used, and these are continually rotating at enormously high speeds day and night. If they should run down, the electric current in your house would go dead. Even in an electric battery where there is no apparent motion, chemical reactions take place and produce very high motion between the molecules and atoms of the liquid.

WHAT GOOD IS THIS STATIC ELECTRICITY?

By this time you are probably thinking that this static electricity is a very queer and useless kind. It isn't at all like the electricity that flows through wires to light lamps, ring door bells, run vacuum cleaners and washing machines and does a thousand and one other useful things. You can't do any of these things with static electricity. All it seems to be good for is to make things magnetic. It doesn't seem to be good for anything else. This, of course, is not true. If you scrape your feet along the carpet again and instead of touching the wall with a card you touch some metal with your finger you'll soon discover that this kind of electricity is very real. You'll get a shock as you see a bright spark leap from your finger to the metal. And while you think that this spark, which only lasts a fraction of a split second, is totally useless, you may be surprised to know that without it or the kind of electricity it represents, radio and television would be impossible. So you see that static electricity is quite important after all.

HOW DOES THIS SPARK MAKE RADIO POSSIBLE?

Your eyes are much too slow to see what actually happens when the spark leaps from your finger to the metal. It all goes so terribly fast that it looks just like an instant flash. But what actually takes place is quite interesting. The spark leaps back and forth, back and forth, back and forth perhaps a thousand times in that split second; and in doing so it sends out tiny, weak and invisible electric waves which are the same as radio waves. These waves, invisible and weak as they are, travel at a speed of 186,000 miles per second through doors, windows, walls, ceilings and everything else and, when produced continually and intensified ten thousand times, they form the only connecting link between the broadcasting studio and your radio or television set.

WHY DOES RUBBING PRODUCE ELECTRICITY? WHAT IS ELECTRICITY?

Just what is this different kind of magnetism which we call *static electricity* and why does it appear on combs and cards and other objects when we rub them? How does it enable them to attract light objects like salt grains and hairs and tissue paper? And how does it differ from the kind of electricity we are all familiar with—the kind that flows through wires and into our homes to perform all the amazing tasks that electricity does? What is it all about, and how and why does it work?

In order to answer these questions and many more like them we shall take a little trip into the inside of matter and try to find out what it is made of and why it behaves the way it does. Only when we understand what all matter is made of can we hope to understand electricity.

THE INVISIBLE WORLD INSIDE OF MATTER

Everything in the entire universe, regardless of what it is or where it is, is made up of trillions of billions of invisible specks called ATOMS. Everybody today has read something about atoms and knows that the breaking up of the atom is what made the atom bomb possible. But not everyone knows how nature has constructed the atoms and how in spite of their differences, they are all built from the same material.

Fifty years ago it was believed that the atom was the smallest particle in nature. It was called "the brick which builds everything in the universe." There are 92 different kinds of natural atoms which we call elements. They are called elements because they form the fundamental building blocks of nature. Of course you are familiar with many of these elements like gold, silver, lead, oxygen, hydrogen, tin, iron and many many others. These elements combine with one another to form all of the compounds in the world, compounds like water, salt, wood, paper and millions and millions of others. The atoms of these elements are, of course, all different just as the compounds are all different. Just as a compound like a piece of chalk is different from a compound like a chunk of wood, so the element oxygen is different from the element gold. Just as water is different from sand, so hydrogen is different from tin. Just as glass is different from rubber, so nitrogen is different from zinc. Years ago, scientists knew why compounds differed from one another. They correctly said it was due to the different number and arrangement of the atoms in the molecules.

A molecule is the smallest division of a compound while an atom is the smallest division of an element. Molecules are always made up of two or more atoms. A molecule of water contains three atoms; two of hydrogen and one oxygen. A molecule of wood contains about 21 atoms and so on. There is no such thing as an atom of water or an atom of wood or an atom of any compound because atoms make up compounds and there are only 92 natural atoms or elements while there are millions and millions of compounds.

But why the atoms of the elements which were thought to be indivisible, differed among themselves was another thing. If atoms can't be divided up, why are the elements all different? It was then that scientists started to study the atom more carefully.

WHAT GOES ON INSIDE THE ATOM

To get some idea of how small an atom, any atom at all, really is, think of it as the size an orange would appear if you could see it twenty miles away. Or the next time you drink a glass of milk, just remember that there are more atoms in that milk than there are drops of water in the Pacific ocean. That means that the atom is pretty small, doesn't it? Nobody has yet been able to see what an atom looks like, but we know a great deal about it in spite of not being able to see one. Small as the atom is (and more than a hundred million will fit on the head of a pin with plenty of room to spare) it is mostly empty space! It is quite like an inconceivably tiny universe, for it has a center called the NUCLEUS and a number of particles revolving around this center like the planets around the sun, only thousands of times faster.

Believe it or not, this central core which we call the nucleus is less than one trillionth the size of the atom itself. The particles that go whizzing around this nucleus have plenty of room to do so because, as we just said, the atom is mostly empty space.

Packed into the nucleus so that they can't easily get out, are a number of positive (+) electrical charges called PROTONS and a number of neutral particles called NEUTRONS. The number of these protons that are *inside* the nucleus determine what the element is to be. That is the ONLY thing that determines the element. Hydrogen has 1 proton inside its nucleus, iron has 50, uranium has 92 and so on. It is very important to remember that these protons are + charges "locked up" inside the tiny nucleus along with the neutrons. No two different elements have the same number of protons locked up inside of their nuclei.

ELECTRONS PLAY THE LEADING ROLE IN THE DRAMA OF ELECTRICITY

Revolving around this central nucleus of protons and neutrons, at very high speeds, are inconceivably tiny invisible particles which have negative charges (—) called ELECTRONS and it is these electrons that play the star role in the drama of electricity. They are *all important,* so we have to discuss them pretty

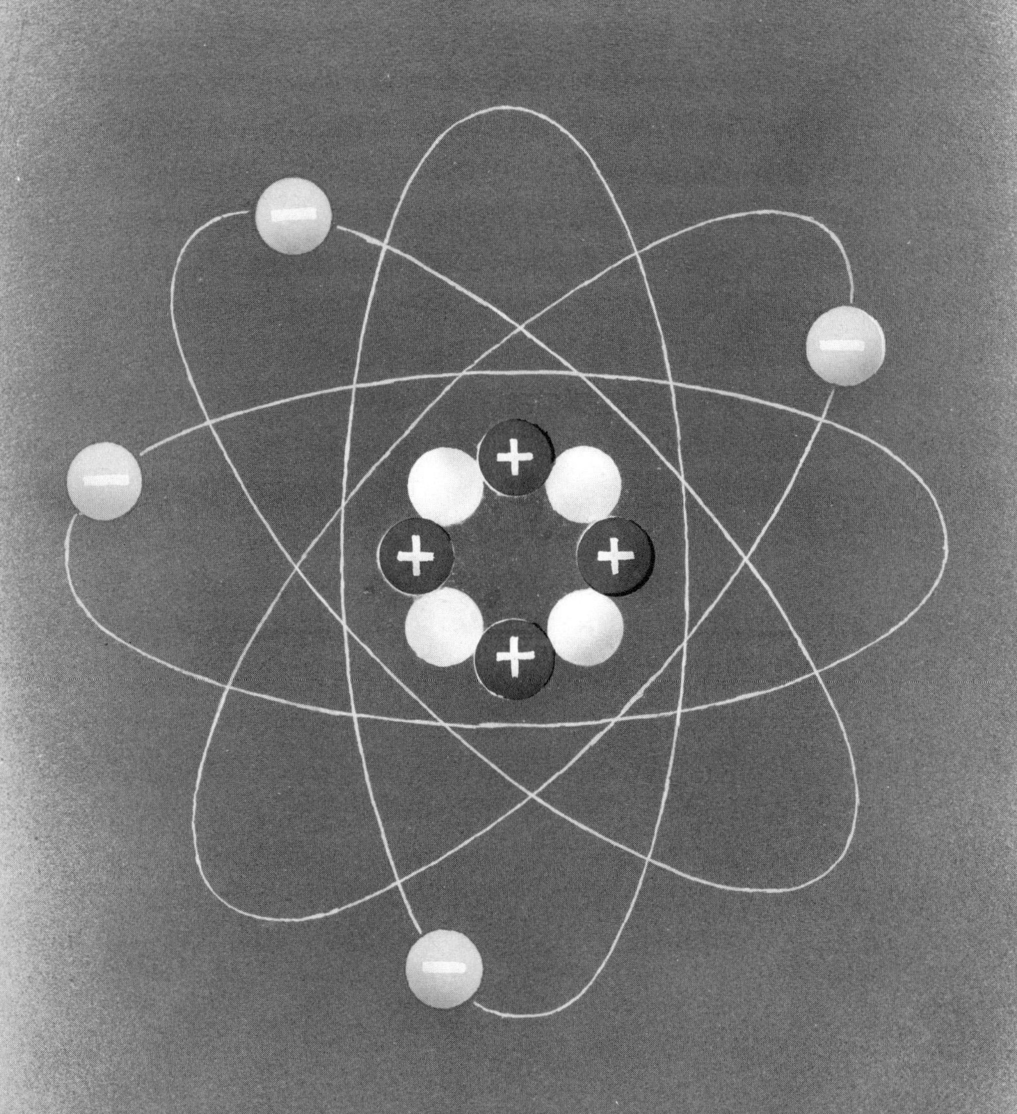

thoroughly and understand their nature and actions if we ever can hope to understand what electricity is and how it works. Electrons are so important that they form the backbone of modern electrical engineering and the study of their behavior under various conditions is called ELECTRONICS.

Electrons are *negative* charges and they are always in motion. They whirl around and around the nucleus in many different rings or orbits and never stop their amazing and varied motions. They are naturally attracted to the protons in the nucleus because the protons are the opposite charge and, you remember, unlike poles or charges attract each other. But while the protons are locked inside of the nucleus and can't get out, the electrons go whizzing around *outside* the nucleus and are relatively free to leave the atom at any time. They are free to escape from the atom and that is exactly what they do. They can be rubbed off your hair and onto a comb, for example, or they can be rubbed off a card or anything else. But there must be rubbing or some other kind of friction or heat to set these electrons free and allow them to attach themselves to other objects.

WHAT HAPPENS WHEN ELECTRONS ESCAPE FROM ATOMS?

Most of the things we see and use and play with are electrically neutral. They do not have any kind of charge, either + or —. When anything is neutral there are just as many electrons outside of the nucleus as there are protons inside the nucleus. The number of electrons just balances the number of protons. In the atoms of practically everything you touch there are just as many electrons whizzing around *outside* the nucleus as there are protons locked up *inside* the nucleus. This means that the MINUS charges just neutralize the PLUS charges. You can see now that as soon as electrons leave the atoms of anything there are more + charges remaining in those atoms than there are — charges and so that thing will no longer be neutral but will take on a + charge. The same is true if there are more — charges in the atoms of anything than there are + charges. That thing will no longer be neutral but will take on a — charge.

Now you'll understand why the comb which you ran through your hair and which instantly became magnetic was charged with negative electricity. To start off with, the comb was entirely neutral just like everything else around you. The electrons outside the nucleus of its atoms just balanced or neutralized the protons inside the nucleus.

But as soon as you rubbed the comb through your hair and rubbed it quickly and briskly, billions of electrons "rubbed off" your hair and on to the comb, leaving the comb with more — charges than + charges. So the comb became negatively charged. As soon as you brought it near those light objects, the field of — electricity which the comb set up around it attracted all the positive charges in the atoms of light objects and the opposites came together instantly just the way the magnet attracts needles and nails. That is why the comb attracted the paper or the salt grains. That is why mostly anything that does not conduct electricity (any non-conductor) will attract light objects to it when rubbed.

If a conductor of electricity is heated in a vacuum, electrons will also be removed from it. This very important fact is responsible for the hundreds of different kinds of vacuum tubes that are on the market today. It is the rapid flow of electrons through a wire grid, between the + and – terminals of a vacuum tube that makes possible such important inventions as radio and television.

VACUUM TUBES

The flow of billions and trillions of electrons away from a heated wire is one of the most important discoveries of this century. This flow can be used and controlled only if the wire is heated in a vacuum where there is practically no air. Air molecules will knock electrons every which way. The vacuum tube is made in many different forms. Each form is used for a different purpose yet they are all based on the same principle. In all vacuum tubes there is always a heated wire called a filament and a plate that is constantly being charged with positive electricity. This gives the tube the appearance of a very odd looking electric light bulb. When the metal filament starts to heat up and glow, electrons are driven off at an enormous rate and are attracted over to the positively charged plate, since opposite charges always attract. It is this steady flow of negatively charged electrons from the hot filament to the positively charged plate that we control in any manner we wish, and by doing so we can intensify the very weak radio waves that enter our set and make them strong enough to be effective in the loud speaker.

One of the most important vacuum tubes and one that works on a different principle from the regular vacuum tube is known as the PHOTO CELL because it is affected by light. Everyone knows that when light strikes a photographic film something happens to the emulsion because it turns black. The light actually effects the atoms in the silver salt used in developing the photo. In the same way when light strikes the clean surface of the element called CESIUM it actually sets billions of trillions of electrons in the atoms of that element free and, in doing so, it creates an electric current. The greater the intensity of the light the stronger will be the current, and the very slightest variation in light will cause the slightest variation in current. This fact is vital in the sending of television waves into your TV set and enabling you to sit comfortably and watch your favorite TV program.

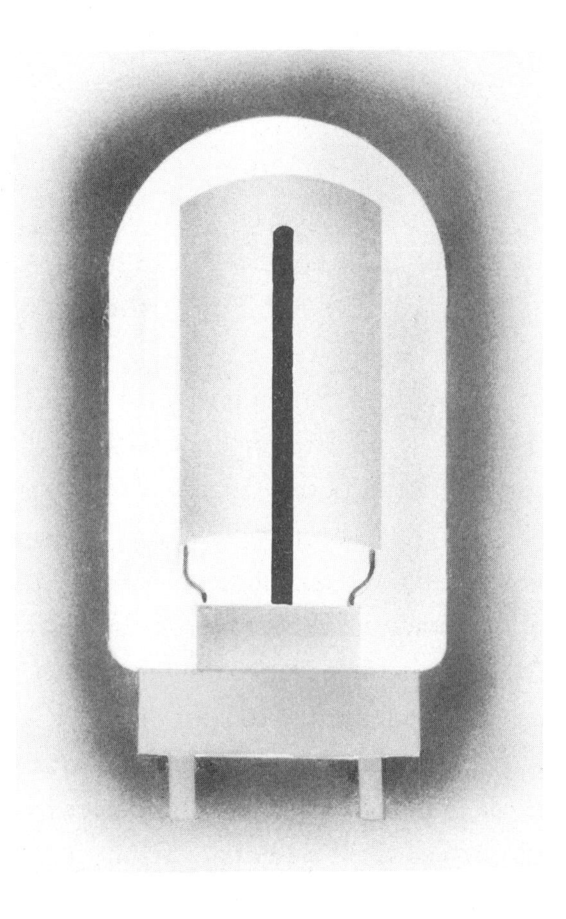

The photo cell is just the reverse of the electric light bulb. The electric light bulb uses electricity to produce light while the photo cell uses light to produce electricity. There are hundreds of different uses for this amazing photo cell.

WHAT IS ELECTRIC CURRENT?

Many people think electric current is the flow of electrons along a wire at the speed of light, but this is not true. It is a very slow movement of electrons in the atoms of a wire or other piece of metal and it is not as simple as many people believe. Perhaps that is one reason why it is so fascinating. To understand it we should know a little about energy.

If you squeeze a sponge as tight as you can you exert energy in doing so. Strangely enough this energy that you exert goes right into the sponge and as soon as you release the sponge you will see it expand. It will actually *move* back to its original size. So the sponge, in moving, released the pent-up energy that you gave to it when you squeezed.

The same thing is true when you wind a clock. You do a certain amount of work in winding the spring and so you give the clock enough pent-up energy to run for a day or a week as the case may be. This pent-up energy is called POTENTIAL ENERGY. Potential energy plays an important part in the electric current as we shall see.

The study of current is divided into: ENERGY, INTENSITY and RESISTANCE. The energy of a current is called the "electric force," more commonly known as the "electromotive force." It is very similar to a pump which lifts water all the way from a deep well, up to a tank on the roof of a house. The pump works continually, and the more work it does the more water it will lift against gravity, all the way up to that tank on the roof. Now it is easy to understand that the water in that high tank contains a great deal of pent-up energy, and if it were released and allowed to spill out or flow through a pipe toward the ground it would certainly do so. The higher the tank is, the faster the water falls or flows through the pipe, just as the higher a waterfall is above the ground the faster and more forcibly the water falls to the ground. But the higher the tank is, the harder the pump must work to get the water to it and the more energy it must exert. So the energy of the pump and the work it does in lifting water against gravity is transferred to the water up in the tank. The pent-up energy of the water in the tank is called potential energy because, while it may be still and quiet in the tank, it will rush out and spill out and fall or flow toward the ground as soon as it is released.

Now suppose that, instead of a pump, we had a dynamo which generates electricity. And suppose that, instead of a pipe, we had a long wire connected to the dynamo at one end and to a motor at the other end. The dynamo now takes the place of the pump and the wires take the place of the pipe. The dynamo is constantly exerting energy just the way the pump did. Its wheel is going around and around, same as the wheel of the pump. But, instead of lifting water, it is constantly freeing electrons from the rest of the atoms in the wire just as you did when you rubbed the comb through your hair, only it is doing it much harder and much faster and it doesn't let up. This takes a lot of work and energy

and this energy is turned into electrical energy. Each electron that is set free from one atom in the wire grabs on to the atom next to it and makes up for the loss of the electrons that left it. The electrons in this atom in turn grab on to the next atom and make up for the loss of the electrons that left it and so on all along the wire. It is very much like a bucket brigade at a small town fire, where a hundred men form a line and pass buckets of water from one to the other. The buckets keep on moving along the line of men and the water from each bucket in turn is thrown on the fire. The electrons are forced through the atoms in the wire in much the same way that each invisible particle of water is forced through the

pipe when flowing from the tank to the ground. This forcing of electrons in the wire, due to the forcing power of the dynamo, is called electromotive force and is indicated by the initial E. It is measured in VOLTS. The volt was named for Alessandro Volta, an Italian scientist. Just as the water in the pipe increases in speed as the pump increases in speed, so the electrons in the wire increase in speed and intensity as the wheel of the dynamo increases in speed, and the magnetism of the dynamo increases in strength.

The CURRENT STRENGTH, or INTENSITY of a current is merely the number of electrons that pass a given point in the wire in one second. One AMPERE (named for André Ampère, a French scientist who discovered it) is the passage of about two million, million, million electrons past any given point. In other words, when current is flowing through a wire at the rate of 2,000,000,000,-000,000,000 electrons every second we have only one Ampere of current strength. This is like saying that when water is flowing through the pipe at the rate of 2,000,000 drops per second we have a certain unit of flow of water.

Now let us go back to the pipe that connects the tank high up on the roof with the ground. The water in that pipe rubs against the inner wall of the pipe and the friction, of course, slows down the flow. This friction is called RESISTANCE and the more resistance there is to the flow of the water the slower it will flow. If the pipe were corroded and rusty, there would be still more friction inside, and the water would flow more slowly than it would flow in a new pipe. If we had a number of pipes all with different insides, offering more or less resistances to the flow of the water, we should have that many different speeds of flow.

The same thing is true in metals. The electrons, in moving from one atom to the other in a metal, meet with resistance, due entirely to the make-up of the atoms in that metal. Some metals offer more resistance to the passage of these electrons than others do. Silver offers the least resistance and copper comes next. These metals are called good CONDUCTORS. The metals tin and lead offer the most resistance and are called poor conductors among the metals. Since silver is too expensive for wiring, nearly all wire is made of copper. Just as there always will be some friction inside of a pipe as the water flows through it, so there always will be some resistance in a metal or wire as the current flows through it. This resistance is measured in OHMS (named for George Simon Ohm, a German physicist and mathematician). Now there is a very simple relation between the electromotive force, the current and the resistance.

This relationship says that the current, called intensity and indicated by the letter I (measured in amperes) is equal to the electromotive force (measured in volts) divided by the resistance (measured in ohms) or, to use the initials, we have: $I = E/R$
and this very important relation is known as OHM'S LAW.

Now the question that you will probably want to ask is: if electrons travel so slowly inside the atoms of a metal when there is a current flowing through the metal, how do you account for the great speed of electricity—we know that it travels 186,000 miles per second, same as light does. What really happens when you turn on the current is that all the electrons in all of the atoms of that wire are "alerted" instantaneously. It is this so-called alert signal that travels with the speed of light. To make this clearer suppose you had a long line of soldiers standing at ease. Now suppose the captain shouts "attention" and all the soldiers obey at once. You would see the entire line come to attention instantaneously in somewhat the same way that the atoms in the wire "come to attention." Now suppose that the command were for each soldier to pass his gun to the soldier on his left. This, also, would be carried out instantly and you would see guns moving all along the line. While the guns would move slowly from one soldier to the next, the entire effect of all the guns moving would be instantaneous. The same is true for the electron movement in the atoms of the wire. They all move at once like the soldiers' guns but they travel from one atom to the next quite slowly.

HOW DO WE MAKE AN ELECTRIC CURRENT?

There are two ways of making an electric current: CHEMICALLY and MECHANICALLY. The first method gives us the electric battery and the second method gives us the dynamo or generator. Let us consider the battery first, because it is not only the oldest way of making a current, but it is by far the easiest.

The simplest battery is nothing more than a glass jar filled with dilute sulfuric acid. In one side of the jar we place a strip of pure copper and in the other side a strip of pure zinc. If these two metals are connected by a copper wire as shown in the picture, a current will be set up in that wire and that current may be strong enough to light a small flashlight bulb. The current in this case is caused by rather complex chemical reactions in the acid because of the two different metals in it. It will travel from the copper to the zinc in a steady, but very weak flow. But if the zinc of this battery is connected with the copper of another similar battery, and the zinc of that second battery is again connected to the copper of a third battery as shown in the picture, there will be a considerable current set up—enough to ring a bell or light an automobile lamp. You can make a battery your-

self, but be very careful. The acid is dangerous and will burn you severely if it touches you. Don't pour it yourself; let some older person pour the sulfuric acid into the jar and arrange the two strips of metal. You can have the fun of seeing the current light a small flashlight bulb. You can also make a very tiny and extremely weak battery for yourself from an ordinary lemon. Just cut the lemon in half and put a small piece of copper in it on one side and a small piece of zinc in it on the other side. If you touch the two metals to your tongue you will actually feel a tiny and very weak current. It won't be strong enough to light even a small flashlight bulb but it will be a current nevertheless. The acid of the lemon acts in the same way that the sulfuric acid acts in the battery jar we just described.

WHAT IS THE BATTERY IN YOUR FLASHLIGHT MADE OF?

The battery we have just been discussing is known as a WET CELL because of the liquid acid. Now of course it would be foolish to carry liquid acid in your flashlight—it might spill into your pockets when you carry the flashlight and it could

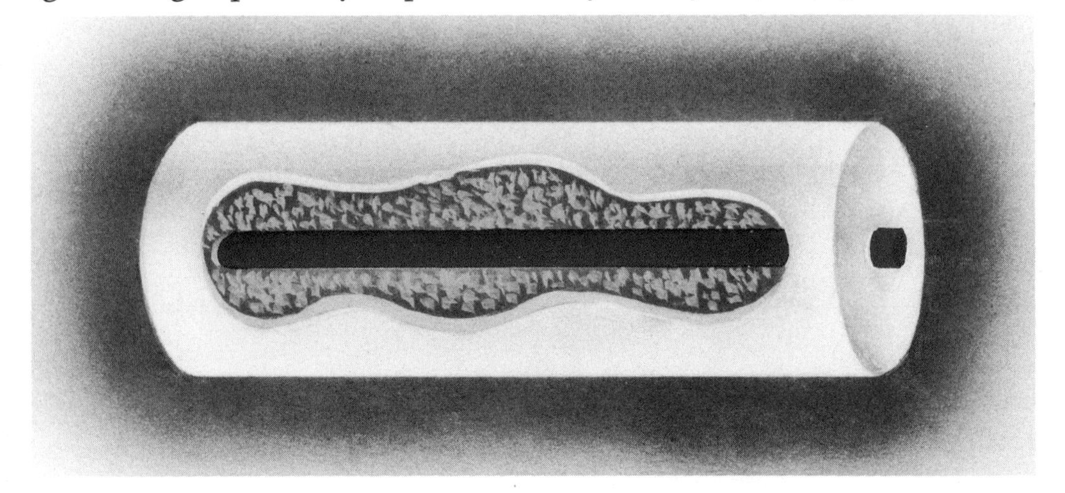

do a lot of damage to your clothing and your skin. The flashlight battery is a DRY CELL battery. The outside container is zinc and the center is usually a small copper rod. The zinc container is filled with carbon grains and a salt called manganese dioxide, soaked in a liquid called ammonium chloride. This mixture which does not form a liquid takes the place of the sulfuric acid in the wet cell battery and we get a current running from the copper to the zinc. Three such batteries in a flashlight holder tube are enough to light a small bulb brilliantly.

MAGNETISM AND ELECTRICITY WORK TOGETHER LIKE THE BLADES OF A SCISSORS

Wherever one is, the other is sure to be hiding or lurking around. This is just another way of saying that magnetism can be effective electrically, and electricity can be effective magnetically, but in each case you have to *move something*. There must be motion just as there was when you rubbed the comb or scraped your feet on the carpet in doing those tricks. Moving a metal rod or a coil of wire up and down rapidly between the opposite poles of a powerful magnet will produce an electric current in the rod or the coil. As soon as the motion stops, the current stops. The motion of an electric current in the wire wound round and round a piece of iron will transform that iron into a strong magnet. As soon as the current stops the iron loses all its magnetism. In the first case you transform magnetism into electricity, in the second case you transform electricity into magnetism. This close relationship between magnetism and electricity, which was discovered by a Danish professor in 1820, gives us the dynamo and the electromagnet. The professor was Hans Christian Oersted who was lecturing a class on electric batteries. While he was talking he noticed that the needle of a compass he had on his desk did not point to the magnetic north pole—it pointed west. Then he saw that it was resting on a wire from the battery and as soon as he removed it from the wire the needle swung back where it belonged. He correctly concluded that there must be some connection between magnetism and electricity and here was born a new era in civilization. A few years later, in 1824, Michael Faraday, a brilliant scientist, working on Oersted's discovery, produced the very first dynamo and motor and this was followed by the amazing electromagnet, invented in 1829 by Joseph Henry. Without these two inventions we should all be living back in the gas light era and the horse-and-buggy days before the American Revolution.

MAGNETISM MAKES ELECTRICITY

Now let's go back to that horseshoe magnet we talked about in the beginning. You already know that there is an attraction between the opposite poles of this magnet, and the space between the two arms is actually strained by what we call "lines of force." Of course you can't see these lines of force but you can prove to yourself that they are there. Just place a sheet of paper over the magnet and sprinkle some iron filings on the sheet. The direction of these lines of force will be seen instantly. They will show up as clearly as those shown in the picture.

Now it is a fact that the mechanical energy that you exert in moving that rod up and down quickly between the poles of the magnet is transformed into electrical energy. By doing this you are actually producing an electric current in the rod. As long as you keep moving the rod there will be current in it, and the instant you stop, all the current will vanish. Of course, if you were to try this experiment with an ordinary horseshoe magnet and a metal rod, the current that you would produce would be far too weak to be detected. You can't move the rod fast enough and the magnet is much too weak to make any noticeable current in the rod.

THE PRINCIPLE OF THE DYNAMO

This is precisely the principle of the dynamo. The lines of force between the opposite poles of an enormously powerful magnet are constantly being cut by a rotating frame carrying a number of metal rods as shown in the picture. As the frame goes round and round at a terrifically high speed, these rods keep on cutting the lines of force, and a strong current of electricity is set up in the rods. The

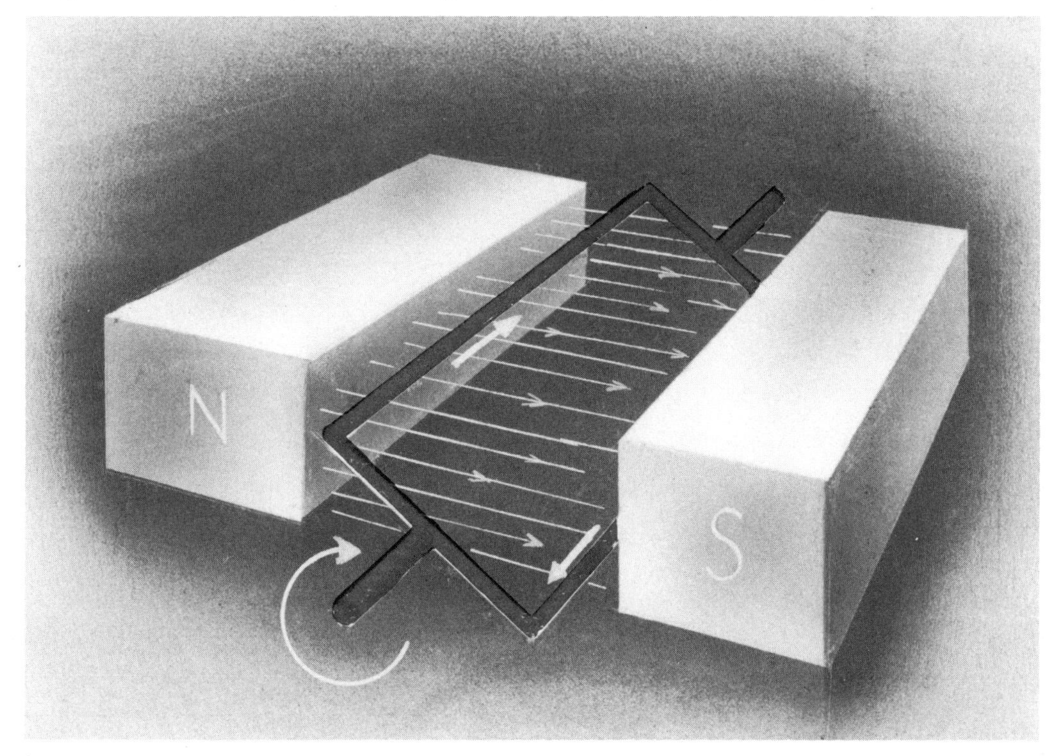

faster the frame rotates and the more powerful the magnet is, the stronger the current will be. It is important to note that as the frame goes round and round, the rods all move *up* on one side and *down* on the other side. When they move up, the current in the rods flows in the opposite direction. In other words the current in the rods is + one split second and — the next split second. This very rapid alternating from + to — and back as much as 60 times per second is called ALTERNATING CURRENT. It is carried away through wires which rub against metal rings attached to the axle of the rotating frame. This is shown in the picture. By means of split rings on the axle of the frame, a current that does not alternate but flows steadily and evenly can be produced by the dynamo. This is called DIRECT CURRENT.

The frame of the modern dynamo is called the ARMATURE. It is usually driven by steam or water power. That is why electric power is so plentiful and cheap in regions where there are great waterfalls. The rings that are attached to the axle of the armature are called COMMUTATORS (in the case of the split ring) and the contact pieces that send the current through the wire are called BRUSHES. The modern dynamo is far too complicated to describe in this book but there are many other books which discuss it in detail.

ELECTRICITY MAKES MAGNETISM

We have just seen how metal rods moving very rapidly in a magnetic field produce electricity. Now we shall see how the electric current, flowing through a metal, sets up a magnetic field and makes a magnet out of any piece of iron that ordinarily is not a magnet. This magnetic effect of the electric current is without doubt one of the most important discoveries ever made. It gives us the electromagnet and without that little gadget most of the electrical instruments would vanish. There could be no telegraph or telephone or radio or television or news ticker or bell or modern dynamos or motors or any other electrical instrument. It is safe to say that nearly everything in the world that is run by electricity has one or more electromagnets connected with it.

The electromagnet is nothing more than a short, round piece of iron like a very thick nail or a heavy bolt, with insulated copper wire wound around and around it. The wire must be wound around the iron in many layers somewhat the way a bolt of twine is wound—the kind of twine you use for flying a kite. The more windings there are around the iron the stronger the magnet will be when a current is sent through the coils of wire. The picture shows you what an electromagnet looks like.

HOW TO MAKE AN ELECTROMAGNET

You can make an electromagnet and see for yourself how it works. Just get an iron bolt and about five yards of insulated copper wire from a hardware store. Bell wire is ideal for the purpose. Now carefully wind this wire around the bolt and, as soon as you have completed the first layer, start the next one but separate the two layers with a piece of tape as shown. Be sure to continue winding the wire in the same direction as the first layer. Keep on adding one layer after another,

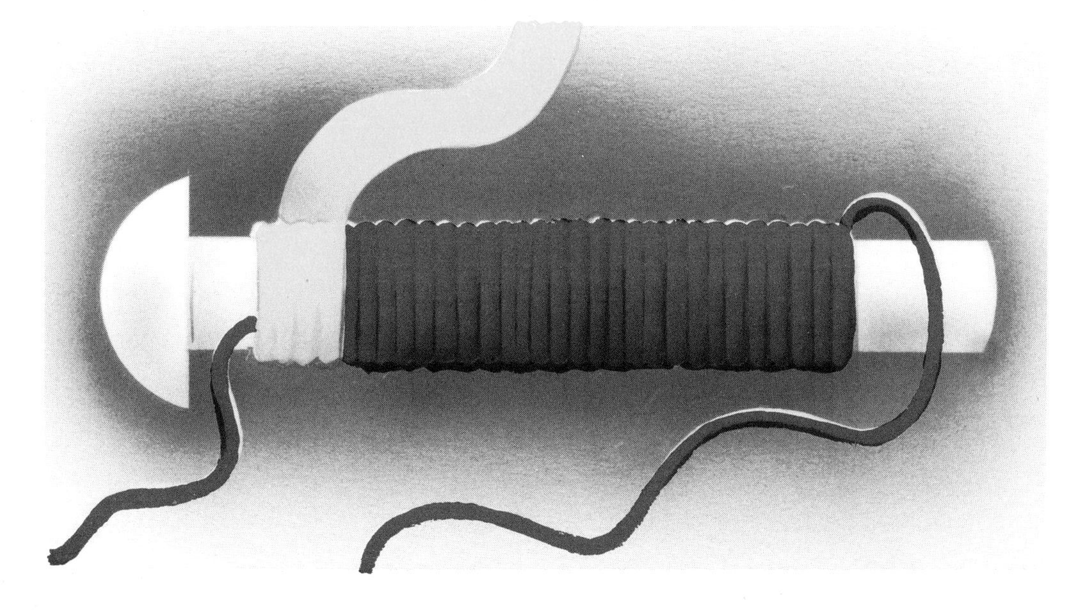

always separating each layer from the next with a small piece of tape. After you have a fairly thick coil of wire wound around bring the iron bolt close to a number of carpet tacks. Nothing will happen because there is no magnetism in the bolt. If now you connect both ends of the coil of wire to two or three strong dry cell batteries, you will see the tacks jump up and cling onto the bolt. As soon as you disconnect the wire from the batteries all the tacks will fall.

The iron is *not* a magnet when there is no current in the coil or wire and *is* a magnet as soon as the current starts to flow through the coil. By putting this knowledge to practical use we are able to enjoy nearly all of the modern conveniences that we have today. This certainly seems strange, doesn't it? How is it that a piece of iron and a coil of wire combine to give us so many wonderful instruments? How can this possibly be? Well, let's investigate.

HOW THE TELEGRAPH WORKS

You can readily see that if you had an electromagnet in Chicago connected to a series of strong batteries and had wires running from those batteries all the way to New York, you could lift a nail or other piece of iron in Chicago merely by completing the circuit in New York. Now you may not want to lift a nail in Chicago but you can see how important this is if, instead of a nail the iron were a flat piece which made a click against the magnet every time you pressed the button in New York. And every time you released the button and shut off the current it made another click. By means of these clicks you can tap out a message for, as you probably have guessed by now, this is the principle on which the telegraph is based. So messages are sent to all parts of the world, thanks to the electromagnet.

Perhaps the most amazing thing about the electromagnet is the limitless speed of its reactions. And no matter how slight the current is it will be recorded by this wonder-magnet. If you had an electromagnet connected with a battery and a switch, and you were able to turn the current on and off one thousand times in a single second, the iron would be a magnet and would lose all of its magnetism one thousand times in that second. Because of this, the electromagnet is entirely responsible for the radio loud speaker, the telephone receiver and television. In

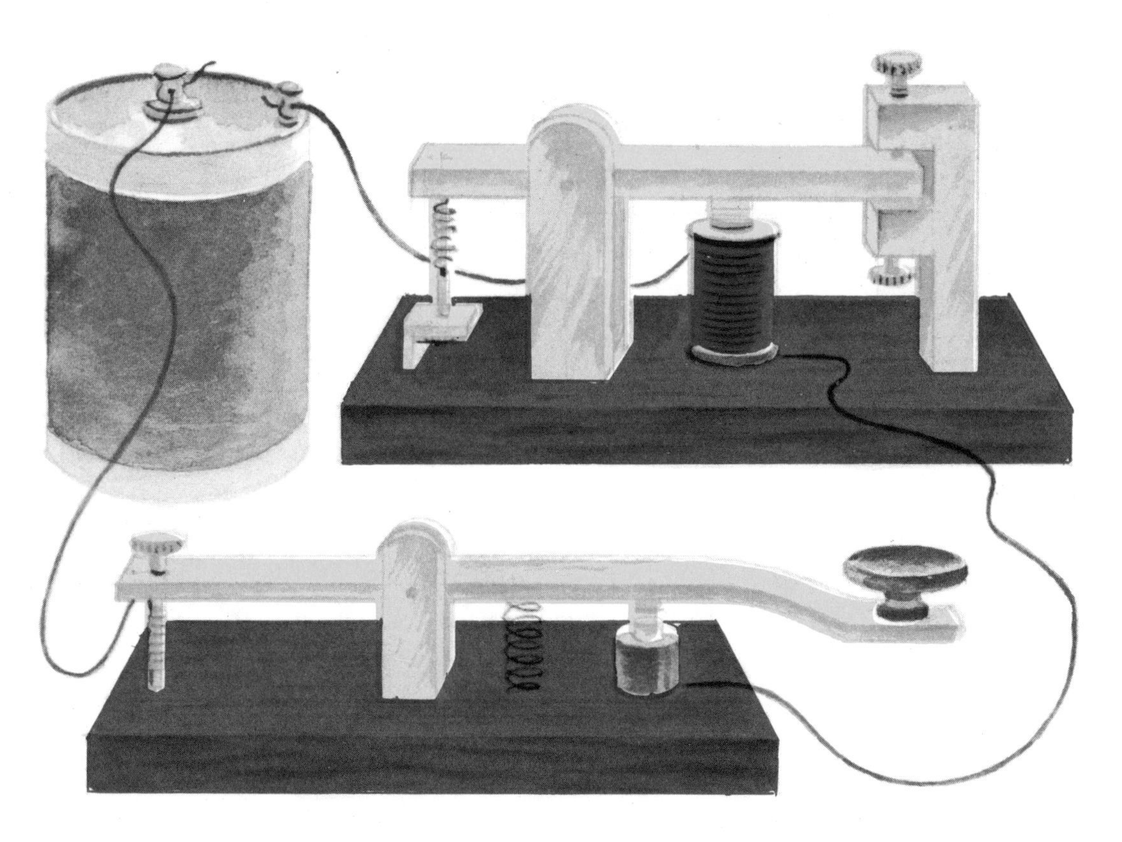

the case of the loud speaker and the telephone receiver a thin steel disc is placed very near the electromagnet. As the current that enters the electromagnet varies in intensity and strength some 400 or 500 times every second, due to the vibrations set up by musical notes or the voice at the other end, the magnet varies in strength just that many times. And so it attracts the disc and makes it vibrate just as the musical notes and the voice vibrates. The disc, then, talks and sings.

Your television set would never give you the entertainment and the pictures that it does if it were not for the faithful guiding of the miraculous cathode ray. This is done with electromagnets. The cathode ray is influenced by a magnet and therefore can be guided by it. Electromagnets cause that ray to sweep the screen of your television set thousands of times every second and produce moving pictures which would otherwise be impossible.

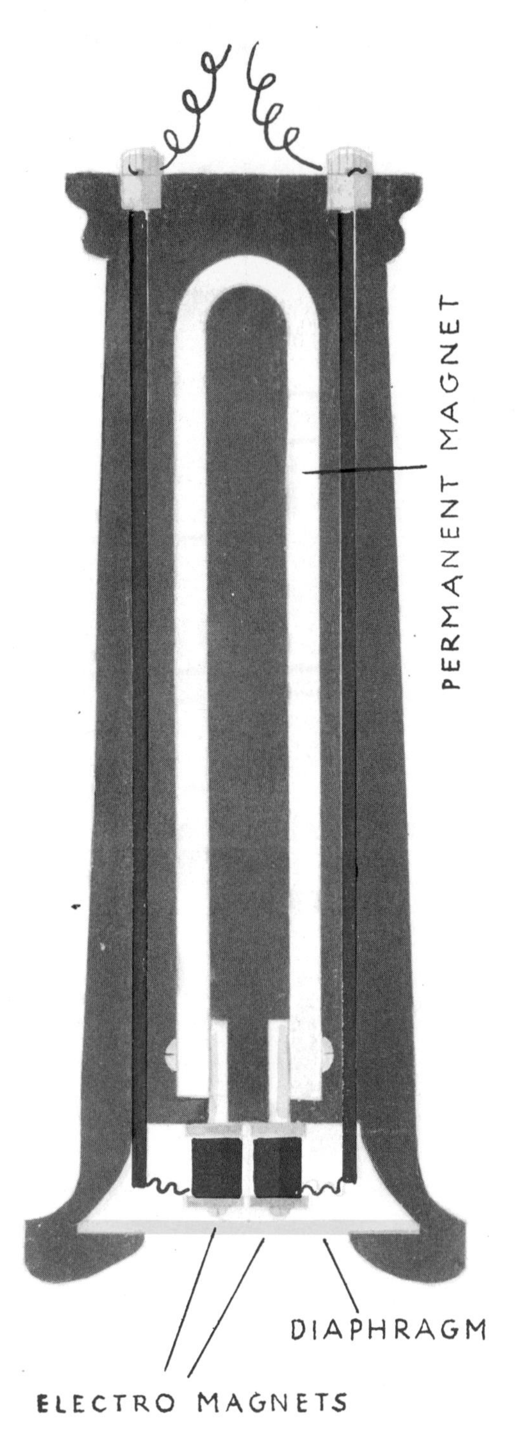

In the electric bell we have an electromagnet close to a bar with a hammer-like knob at the end of it. When the current is on the magnet attracts the bar and causes the knob to hit a gong. But as soon as this happens the circuit is broken and the magnet loses all of its attraction for the bar. Then a spring forces the bar back to where it completes the circuit again and the magnet instantly attracts the bar all over again. But this breaks the circuit and the spring forces the bar back again to where it completes the circuit. This goes on and on making and breaking the circuit and causing the magnet to attract and let loose the bar. Of course the hammer-like knob, hitting the gong each time, rings the bell.

These are only very few of the hundreds of important electrical instruments that would be impossible without the electromagnet. The electric motor alone, with all its hundreds of uses, would take a large book to describe. And the talkies and the news ticker and the modern electric phonograph and block signals on railroads and photographs sent hurling through space and hundreds of other electric wonders of the world we live in —all of these would be impossible with-

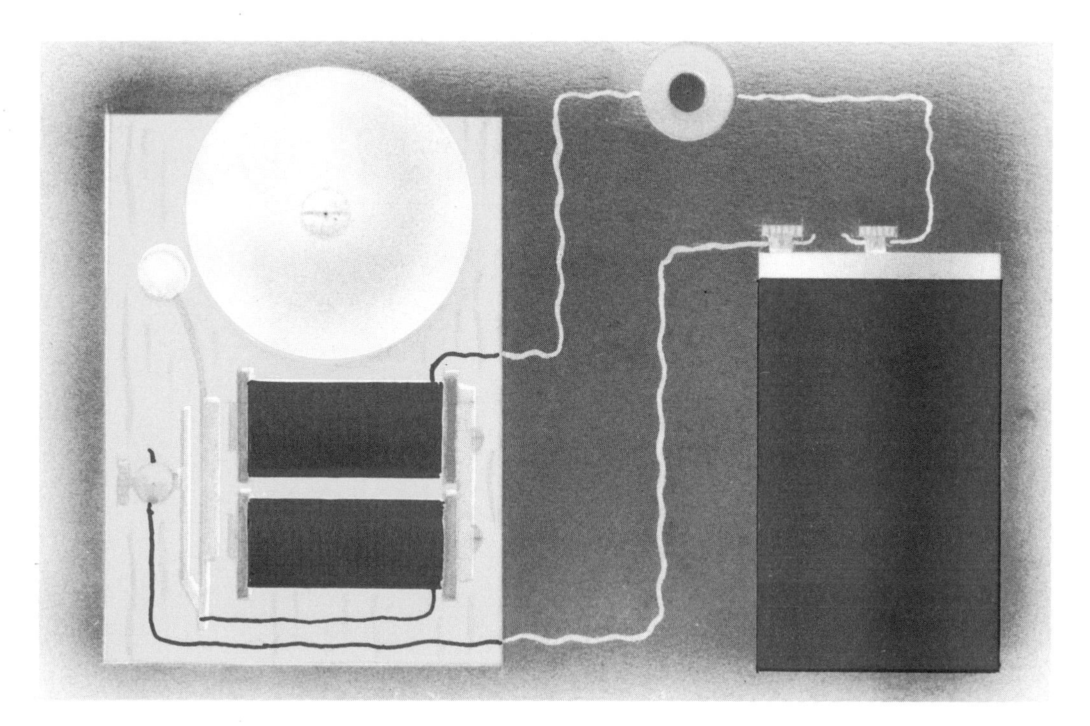

out a coil of wire wound around a piece of iron . . . and an electric current.

And so ends our very short introduction to the study of electricity, the force that runs our world today. A great deal is known today that was unknown fifty years ago but there is still much to learn. The amazing discoveries in atomic energy have opened up a vast new field in electricity. If what you have learned from these few pages, if this very first "look in" on electricity has interested you and given you even the slightest idea of what it's about, we hope that you will be encouraged to study the subject further. Who knows, perhaps YOU may be one of the great scientists of the future who, in the course of tireless research, may discover new and vitally important laws and principles in the vast field of electronics.